This
SpongeBob SquarePants
Annual belongs to

....

CONTENTS

EGMONT
We bring stories to life

First published in Great Britain 2008 by Egmont UK Limited
239 Kensington High Street, London W8 6SA
Created for Egmont by John Brown Publishing Group
Edited by Chloe Martin • Designed by Rebecca Studd and Nick Brown
© 2008 Viacom International Inc. All rights reserved.
Nickelodeon, SpongeBob SquarePants and all related titles, logos
and characters are trademarks of Viacom International Inc. Created by Stephen Hillenburg.

ISBN 978 1 4052 3907 3
1 3 5 7 9 10 8 6 4 2
Printed in Italy

SAY HI TO SPONGEBOB

WELCOME, FANS!

Roll up, roll up! Welcome to the Bikini Bottom Undersea Showcase! And here is the star of the show ... SpongeBob SquarePants!

SpongeBob is a sea sponge who lives in the underwater town of Bikini Bottom. Although our porous friend works as a fry cook at the Krusty Krab restaurant by day, he is also a sponge of many talents.

GASP AT THE PERFECT **PATTY-MAKING!**

WONDER AT THE BRILLIANT **BUBBLE-BLOWING!**

PRESENTING ...
PATRICK!

LOOK AT ME, I'M DANCING!

Starring opposite SpongeBob is his best friend, Patrick Star. Patrick spends his time contemplating difficult philosophical questions that have plagued the greatest minds since the dawn of time. Erm, not really ... Patrick doesn't actually think of anything much.

As you can see, Patrick is able to perform all sorts of emotions ...

JOY

SADNESS

BEWILDERMENT

ALSO STARRING ... SQUIDWARD!

Squidward Tentacles is SpongeBob's grouchy next-door neighbour. A rather unwilling co-star, Squidward dislikes a massive amount of things – and at the top of that list (although they don't realise it) are SpongeBob and Patrick!

I HATE ALL OF YOU.

HERE LIES SQUIDWARD'S HOPES AND DREAMS

However, Squidward is adept at PERFORMING TRAGEDIES

... and he loves INTERPRETIVE DANCE (the audience doesn't, though)

THE SUPPORTING CAST ...

GARY

Gary is SpongeBob's pet snail. He is a snail of few words (well, one word, actually). He knows how to please an audience, though - his party trick is tying shoelaces!

MR KRABS

Mr Krabs is the owner of the Krusty Krab restaurant, and is SpongeBob's boss. There's only one thing he likes ... money! And the only thing he likes to spend it on is his whale of a daughter, Pearl.

MEOW!

THAT'S RIGHT, GARY HAS **FEET!**

GO, PEARL!

SANDY

Sandy Cheeks is Bikini Bottom's resident rodent and super stuntwoman – there's nothing she likes more than doing dangerous stuff. She also has a very special costume – a unique airsuit and helmet, so she can breathe underwater.

PLANKTON

Of course, every show needs its bad guy ... Sheldon J. Plankton is out to steal the secret formula for the Krabby Patty. However, despite his college education, he hasn't yet managed to get it. He lives with Karen his computer wife, who has a Nag Chip installed in her.

WHO ARE YOU CALLING SMALL?

YEE-HA!

CLAM WRESTLING – TEXAS STYLE!

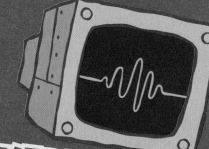

KAREN – A WIRED INTEGRATED FEMALE ELECTROENCEPHALOGRAPH

Never Wash

WORK ON THAT GRIP, SON! ONE DAY YOU'LL HAVE A SHAKE AS STRONG AS MINE!

AND BREATH, TOO.

WOW! A HANDSHAKE FROM MY IDOLS, MERMAID MAN AND BARNACLE BOY!

I'LL NEVER WASH THIS HAND AGAIN...

UH OH.

A FEW DAYS LATER...

HERE'S YOUR DRINK, SIR!

GREAT!

NOW I CAN WASH DOWN THIS DELICIOUS HAND-MADE KRABBY-PATTY!

DRINK UP!

HOLY FISH PASTE! DO YOU COOK WITH THOSE HANDS?!

EWW!

I'M GONNA HURL!

HE HANDLED MY BUN!

YUCK! I'M GONNA CALL THE HEALTH DEPARTMENT!

WAIT! DON'T GO!

BYE! COME BACK SOON!

IF I DON'T DO SOMETHING I'LL BE RUINED!

THINK, KRABS, THINK!

THE END

WACKY WORDS

Can you work out where all these Bikini Bottom characters fit into the grid? Tick the box when you find each one.

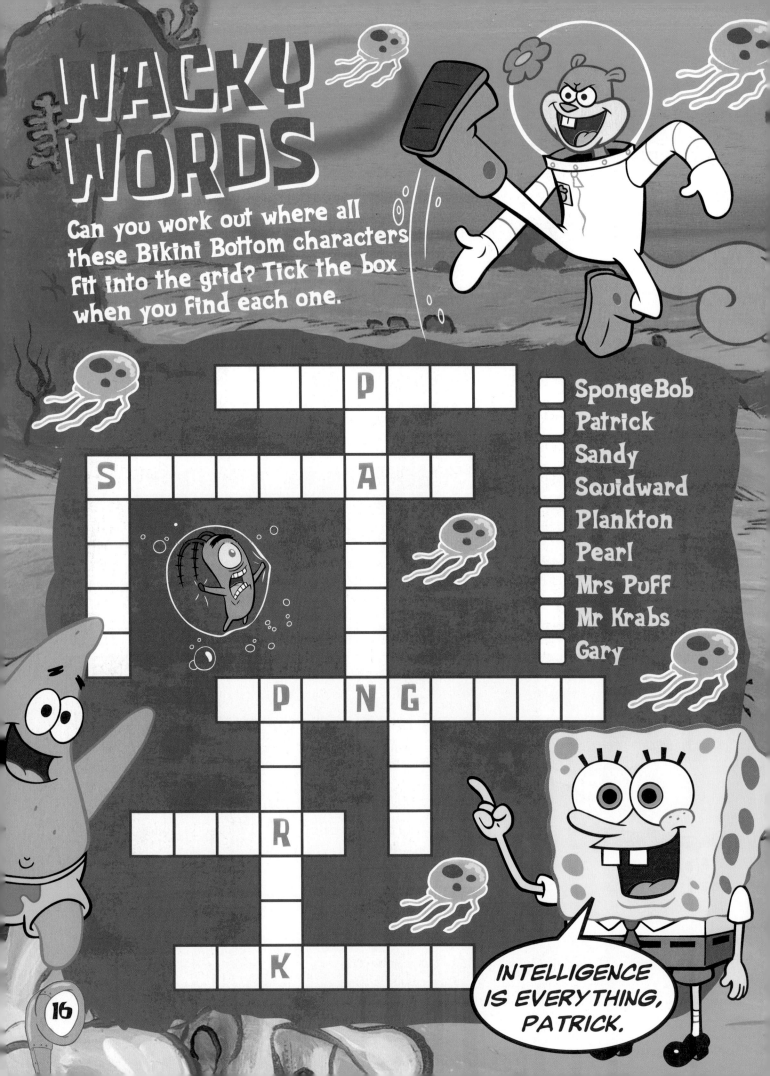

- [ ] SpongeBob
- [ ] Patrick
- [ ] Sandy
- [ ] Squidward
- [ ] Plankton
- [ ] Pearl
- [ ] Mrs Puff
- [ ] Mr Krabs
- [ ] Gary

INTELLIGENCE IS EVERYTHING, PATRICK.

FOOD TRAIL

Gary is hungry! Help him get through the maze to find his food.

START

FINISH

SPONGEBOB DIFFERENTPANTS

All these pictures of SpongeBob look the same – but they're not! Look closely and find the only two that match exactly.

1

2

3

4

5

6

AROUND BIKINI BOTTOM

The underwater town of Bikini Bottom is a treasure trove of watery wonder. Let's take a look around!

Mrs Puff's Boating School

SpongeBob's taken her class many times – but sadly still doesn't have his driving licence.

Conch Street

A quiet, residential street. Well, it would be if it didn't have SpongeBob and Patrick living on it!

Anchor House

Mr Krabs and Pearl reside in this eccentrically shaped abode.

KRUSTY KAREN

WITH THIS BRILLIANT SCHEME, I'M **SURE** TO GET MY HANDS ON THAT KRABBY PATTY RECIPE!

HONEY, YOU NEED A BREAK. WANT TO PLAY A GAME TOGETHER?

STORY BY DAVID LEWMAN PENCILS BY GREGG SCHIGIEL INKS BY JEFF ALBRECHT COLOR BY SNO CONE STUDIOS LETTERS BY COMICRAFT

GAME? WHAT I **WANT** IS FOR YOU TO FINISH CALCULATING HOW BIG A CATAPULT I'LL NEED!

I'M NOT A CALCULATOR! I'M YOUR WIFE!

I'M LEAVING! MAYBE SOMEONE ELSE WILL APPRECIATE ME!

YOU'LL BE BACK! YOU'VE GOT NO PLACE TO GO!

ONE WRITING SESSION LATER...

OH, DARLING KAREN, HEAR MY POEM!

WHY ARE YOU LEANING TOWARD THAT TRASH CAN?

IT...UM... INSPIRES ME.

PSST... PSSST... PSST...

Jellyfishing is great. Blowing bubbles is fun. You're as pretty as a krabby patty, sitting on a bun!

AYE, 'TIS BEAUTIFUL! ≩SNIFF!≩

Since you are not hairy, You're kind of like Gary.

I love you big time. From your shell to your slime.

WELL, WHAT DO YOU SAY, BABY?

YOU JUST COMPARED ME TO A SANDWICH AND A SNAIL. I SAY GET LOST!

ALL RIGHT, I GIVE UP. LET'S GO.

THERE'S SOMETHING ON YOUR HEAD, TRASH CAN PERSON.

PUZZLED WITH PATRICK

Hi! Do you wanna test your brain to the limit? Push it harder than it's ever been pushed before? Well get ready, because these puzzles are even more difficult than spelling ... difficult!

I KNOW WHAT IT IS ... A MESS!

Join the dots to find out what the picture is!

1   12   3   17
2   18   7
16   6
10
20   19
11   4   5
15   14   8
9   13

SpongeBob and I are playing hide and seek. Can you find us?

I'M BEHIND THE SOFA AND SPONGEBOB IS IN THE KITCHEN.

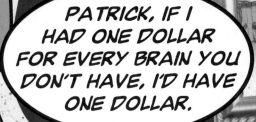

PATRICK, IF I HAD ONE DOLLAR FOR EVERY BRAIN YOU DON'T HAVE, I'D HAVE ONE DOLLAR.

AMAZING MAZE

Avast, me hearties! SpongeBob and Patrick are searching for lost treasure. Find the path through the maze - but be quick, or it'll be the plank for you!

30

SPONGEBOB PIRATEPANTS

Colour in this swashbuckling picture and design your own Bikini Bottom pirate Flag, too!

WRITE IN YOUR PIRATE NAME ....

Story: Walt Dohrn. Art: Jay Lender. Lettering: Sherm Cohen. Coloring: Digital Chameleon. *SpongeBob SquarePants* created by Stephen Hillenburg.

33

PLANKTON'S PLANS

Sheldon J. Plankton has two goals in life: to steal the recipe for the Krabby Patty and to take over the world. So far, both have been unsuccessful. This corrupt copepod has tried everything to get his miniscule mitts on the secret formula ...

BEING EVIL IS TOO MUCH FUN!

1

His first evil scheme was to take over SpongeBob's brain ...

3

He even changed places with Mr Krabs by using Karen's 'switch-lives-just-to-know-what-it's-like-o-mogrifier'.

2

Then he tried to build a robotic Mr Krabs ...

However, each and every one of his devious endeavours has been thwarted (often by an unwitting SpongeBob).

QUAKE IN FEAR, MORTAL FOOLS!

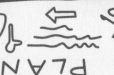

SECRET PLAN #0422614432

Because of Plankton's numerous failures, the Chum Bucket remains the most unsuccessful business venture in Bikini Bottom, with a menu that couldn't tickle anyone's tastebuds. Can you take pity on poor Plankton and come up with a new item for the Chum Bucket's menu? Draw your idea in the space below!

PLANKTON'S PERPLEXING PUZZLES

KNOWLEDGE IS POWER!

Can you find all of Plankton's favourite words in the grid? Words can run forwards, backwards, up, down and diagonally.

YOU CAN TELL HE WENT TO COLLEGE!

BAD	DEPRAVED	INSANE	
CATASTROPHIC	DERANGED	MALEVOLENT	PSYCHOTIC
CORRUPT	DESTRUCTIVE	MANIACAL	VILLAINOUS
CUNNING	DIABOLICAL	MEAN	WICKED
DEMENTED	EVIL	NASTY	ZEALOUS

E	J	S	E	Y	I	Y	D	F	T	L	L	L	Q	D
D	V	U	P	N	T	E	X	N	Q	A	A	I	B	X
C	E	I	S	S	P	S	E	M	N	C	C	V	W	M
P	U	A	T	R	Y	L	A	A	Z	I	A	E	J	O
F	N	N	A	C	O	C	E	N	V	L	I	V	H	N
E	M	V	N	V	U	M	H	N	O	O	N	E	Z	R
V	E	H	E	I	F	R	C	O	E	B	A	Q	E	I
D	N	L	V	Z	N	K	T	Z	T	A	M	D	A	H
J	A	N	J	M	B	G	S	S	B	I	S	E	L	P
M	D	E	G	N	A	R	E	D	E	D	C	M	O	Q
V	I	L	L	A	I	N	O	U	S	D	C	E	U	N
C	O	R	R	U	P	T	B	A	D	T	X	N	S	J
D	E	K	C	I	W	U	A	A	C	I	I	T	N	S
O	T	D	S	L	S	L	B	R	O	V	Q	E	C	X
C	I	H	P	O	R	T	S	A	T	A	C	D	H	C

36

Draw lines to match the members of Plankton's family into pairs.

Which line will lead Plankton to the Krabby Patty?

1
2
3
4

HE'LL NEVER GET THE FORMULA, YOU KNOW ...

SUPER SPOT

Here comes SuperSponge - soaking up crime with his faithful sidekick. These crime scenes look the same, but 15 things are different in picture 2. Can you spot them all?

FINISH IT SHARPISH – THEN BACK TO WORK!

CRAZY CROSSWORD

Have a go at this spectacular Bikini Bottom crossword!

ACROSS

4 Bikini Bottom's beach (3, 6)

7 Mr Krabs' favourite thing (5)

10 SpongeBob lives in a _____ under the sea (9)

11 The shape of SpongeBob's pants (6)

12 The instrument that Squidward plays – badly! (8)

14 Plankton's first name (7)

15 Plankton's restaurant is the _____ Bucket (4)

16 The name of Plankton's computer wife (5)

DOWN

1 SpongeBob's favourite cooking utensil (7)

2 Squidward's last name (9)

3 The Krusty Krab's speciality (6, 5)

5 The only thing Gary says (4)

6 Where Sandy comes from – yee-ha! (5)

8 What SpongeBob and Patrick like to catch in nets (9)

9 SpongeBob's job at the Krusty Krab (3, 4)

13 Mr Krabs' whale of a daughter (5)

43

AT WORK WITH SPONGEBOB

Welcome to the Krusty Krab – the finest eating establishment ever established for eating!

THIS IS WHERE I WORK AS THE TRUSTED FRY COOK. SOMETIMES MR KRABS IS EVEN KIND ENOUGH TO GIVE ME DOUBLE OVERTIME – HE'S THE BEST BOSS A SPONGE COULD ASK FOR! COME ON, LET ME SHOW YOU AROUND ...

Mr Krabs is the owner of the restaurant. This kindly crustacean always puts the customers first.

Ketchup packets
State-of-the-art condiment dispenser units

44

YOU'RE A WORK OF ART ALREADY, PATRICK!

DRAW PATRICK

Grab a pencil and follow these six simple steps!

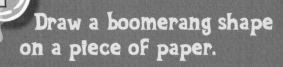

1
Draw a boomerang shape on a piece of paper.

2
Draw a pear shape over the top.

3
Draw a cross through the middle, then add some legs.

4
Give him eyes above the line on either side. Add a mouth below.

5 Carefully rub out the lines. Add eyebrows and a belly button.

6 He's naked! Quickly draw on a pair of patterned shorts.

EVEN I COULD DO IT! MAYBE ...

STORY BY JAY LENDER · PENCILS BY GREGG SHIGIEL · INKS BY JEFF ALBRECHT · COLOR BY SNO CONE STUDIOS · LETTERS BY COMICRAFT

SpongeBob SquarePants

FINGERS!

GO OUT FOR THE *BOMB*, SPONGEBOB!

I *GOT* IT, PATRICK!

WOO!

I AM THE *GRAB*-MASTER!

FAP!

DIVE!

SURE...THAT'S EASY WHEN YOU'VE GOT FINGERS.

HUH?

FINGERS. A GRIPOLOGICAL MUTATION THAT ONLY *YOU* POSSESS.

THESE OLD THINGS? THAT'S SILLY.

I'M NOT KIDDING, MAN, THESE THINGS ARE *WEIRD!*

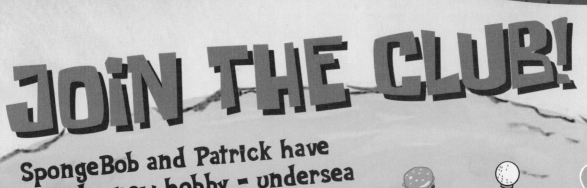

JOIN THE CLUB!

SpongeBob and Patrick have found a new hobby - undersea golfing! Look all around the picture and see how many of each item you can find.

I'M GLAD I BOUGHT TWO PAIRS OF TROUSERS, PATRICK - BECAUSE I'VE GOT A HOLE IN ONE!

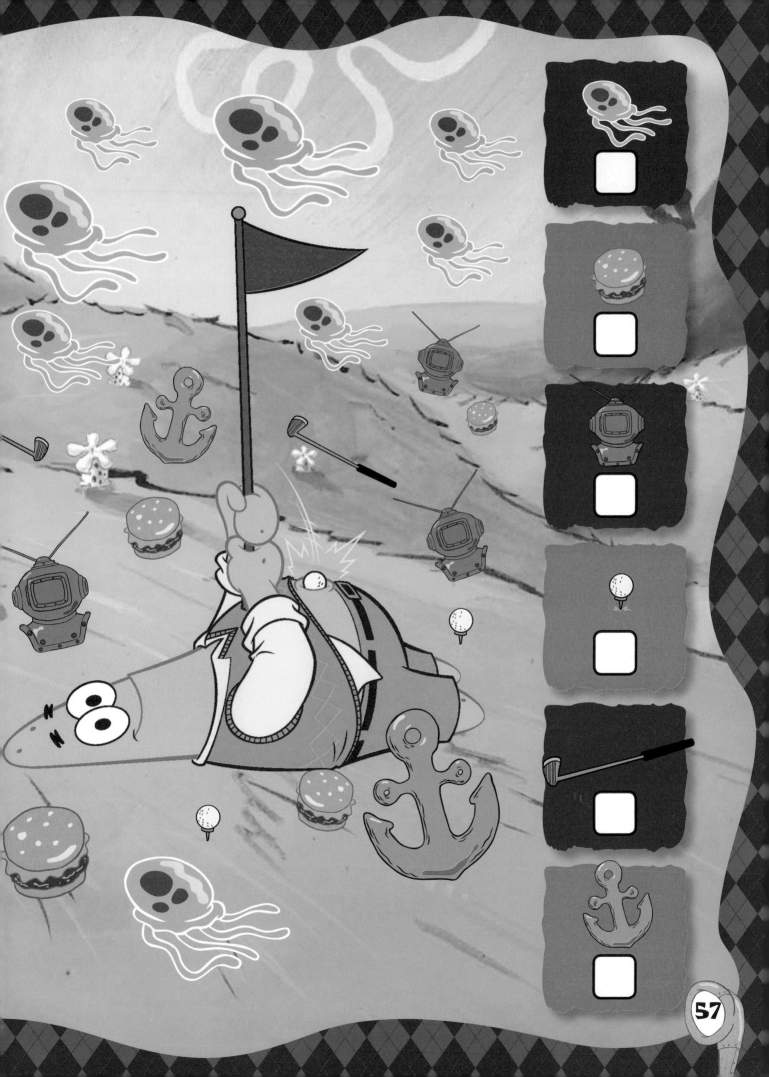

GO WEST!

SpongeBob RanchPants and Sheriff Star are on patrol! Look at the picture and try to spot the matching shadow.

HOWDY, PARTNER!

QUESTION TIME

Ahoy, landlubbers! Test your nautical knowledge with this crazy quiz!

I WILL RULE YOU ALL!

1

Whose favourite activities include clam wrestling and karate?

a) Sandy ☐

b) Squidward ☐

2

What is Patrick's last name?

c) Star ☐

d) Sea ☐

3

What is the name of SpongeBob's street?

e) Conch Street ☐

f) Perch Street ☐

4

What does Plankton want the recipe for?

g) The Triple Gooberberry Surprise ☐

h) The Krabby Patty ☐

5

What is Squidward's job at the Krusty Krab?

i) Cashier ☐

j) Dish washer ☐

6

What is Mr Krabs' favourite thing?

k) Money ☐

l) Honey ☐

7

What does Squidward call his beloved clarinet?

m) Clary ☐

n) Netty ☐

60

Hairy House

I'M BACK FROM WORK, GARY!

IT'S TIME FOR YOUR WALK.

GREAT HAIRDO!

MEOW!

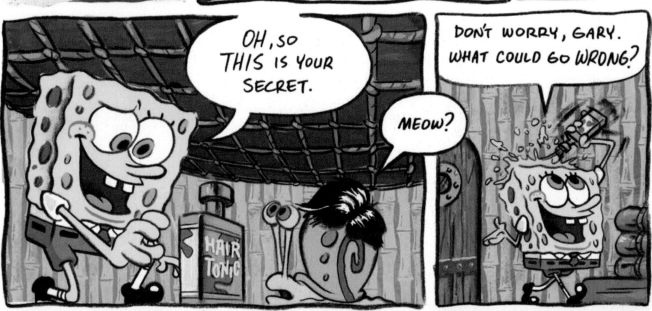

OH, SO THIS IS YOUR SECRET.

MEOW?

DON'T WORRY, GARY. WHAT COULD GO WRONG?

Story: Paul Tibbitt. Pencils and inks: Erik Wiese. Coloring: Nick Jennings. Lettering: Sherm Cohen. *SpongeBob SquarePants* created by Steve Hillenburg.

PUZZLED WITH PATRICK

Wow, you're back for more? Looks like you really love doing hard stuff, so have a go at these. But watch out, they're tougher than a clam's shell!

MY BRAIN HURTS!

Which line will lead SpongeBob to the Krabby Patty?

1 2 3 4

IT'S D! SQUIDWARD'S GONE OUT SHOPPING. IN ALL THE OTHERS HE'S IN THE KITCHEN.

Look at the pictures and find the one that's different.

A B C D E

Frantic Feet

ANSWERS

16

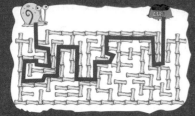

17

Pictures 4 and 6 are the same.

30

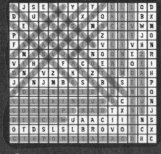

36-37

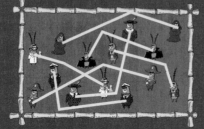

Line 3 leads to the Krabby Patty.

40

42-43 Across - 4: Goo Lagoon 7: Money 10: Pineapple 11: Square 12: Clarinet 14: Sheldon 15: Chum 16: Karen Down - 1: Spatula 2: Tentacles 3: Krabby Patty 5: Meow 6: Texas 8: Jellyfish 9: Fry cook 13: Pearl

56 There are 12 jellyfish, 6 Krabby Patties, 5 diving helmets, 9 golf balls, 7 golf clubs and 5 anchors.

58-59 E is the correct shadow. Line 4 leads to Mystery.

60-61 1: Sandy (a) 2: Star (c) 3: Conch Street (e) 4: The Krabby Patty (h) 5: Cashier (t) 6: Money (k) 7: Clary (m) 8: Larry (p) 9: Tying shoelaces (r) 10: Karen (t) 11: An anchor (u) 12: Mermaid Man and Barnacle Boy (w) 13: Mrs Puff (z).

Patrick is Gary's cousin.